Ken Wilson-Max

Lenny and Wilbur

Alanna Max

Lenny and Wilbur are
the best of friends.

**Best friends
have fun together!**

It's Wilbur's bath day today!
"Ask him to sit." Mummy says.

"Sit!" says Lenny.
Wilbur sits

First some warm water
to wet his fur.

"Then shampoo,
to wash it clean."
says Mummy.

Wilbur shakes.
Lenny giggles.

Best friends
laugh together!

Lenny rubs
Wilbur's tummy
and brushes
his fur.

Wilbur gets a treat.
"Good doggy!" says Mummy.
"Good doggy!" says Lenny.

Best friends eat together.

"Good boy, Lenny!" says Mummy.

"Good boy, Wilbur!" says Lenny.

Wilbur tickles Lenny's ear.
Is it time for a song?

Old McDonald had a farm
Hee-hi hee-hi ho!

And on that farm he had a dog
Hee-hi hee-hi ho!

With a Woof Woof here
And a Woof Woof there

Here a Woof, there a Woof
Everywhere a Woof Woof!

Old McDonald had a farm
Hee-hi hee-hi ho!

When they are finally tired,
best friends rest together.